LEGO STAR WARS

BRICK ADVENTURES
6 ACTION-PACKED, ILLUSTRATED STORIES!

Published by Scholastic Inc., *Publishers since 1920*. SCHOLASTIC and associated logos are trademarks and/or registered trademarks of Scholastic Inc.

This book is a work of fiction. Names, characters, places, and incidents are either the product of the author's imagination or are used fictitiously, and any resemblance to actual persons, living or dead, business establishments, events, or locales is entirely coincidental.

ISBN 978-1-338-33771-6

10 9 8 7 6 5 4 3 2 1   19 20 21 22 23

Printed in China   95
First printing 2019

Book design by Cheung Tai

BRICK ADVENTURES
6 ACTION-PACKED, ILLUSTRATED STORIES!

AWESOME JEDI TALES

by Ace Landers

SCHOLASTIC INC.

CONTENTS

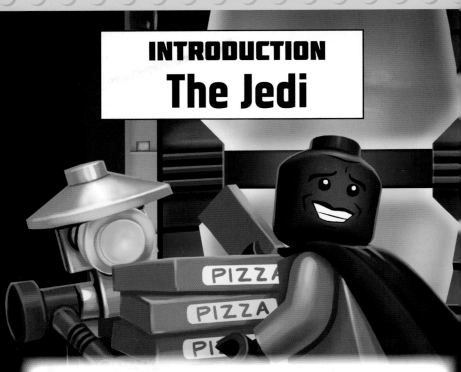

INTRODUCTION
The Jedi

The Jedi have existed for centuries as a noble order of protectors united in their devotion to the light side of the Force, and love of a good, large pizza. In this collection of six adventures, you'll get to hear three stories about the Jedi from Luke Skywalker himself, followed by three from trainee turned champion of the First Order Kylo Ren. It's a laugh-out-loud, action-packed collection of awesome Jedi tales!

INTRODUCTION
The Sacred Texts!

Hi, I'm **Luke Skywalker**, here to take you on a very special journey through legends of the Jedi! There's a story about young me, a story about old me, and even a story about my dear old dad and his Master, Obi-Wan. So, what are you waiting for? Let's dive in!

LUKE AND HIS REY OF SUNSHINE

On a distant planet known as **Ahch-To**, the morning sun rose and so did an old Jedi, Luke Skywalker.

Luke was a legendary Jedi Master, and he'd been hiding on this faraway planet for years when Rey, a young, **Force**-sensitive woman, had found him and asked him to train her. With a stretch and a yawn, he barely had time to wake up before **Rey** stormed into his stone hut.

"Is it time to train yet?" she asked.

"No," said Luke. "It's time to eat."

A giant, hairy beast walked into his hut. It was Chewbacca, a **Wookiee** and old friend to Luke Skywalker. He knelt down and began fixing the door to Luke's hut, which was just a simple curtain (Chewie ripped off the old door).

"Ah, thanks, Chewie," Luke said. "Though maybe I should get a real door instead?"

"Here, let me help," Rey said. She helped Chewie reattach the curtain to the door frame.

Rey was an amazing student, but she lacked patience, which was a very important Jedi value. Seeing her work with Chewbacca gave him an idea.

Luke spoke up. "Actually, I have a very important challenge for you today, Rey."

Rey jumped. "Anything! You name it, Master Skywalker! Do you want me to lift a spaceship into the air? Balance on one hand while you balance on my leg in the air?"

"What? No." Luke shook his head. "Don't be silly. I want you . . . to help Chewie around the island."

Rey's eyebrows lifted in confusion. "You mean . . . help Chewie . . . train to be a Jedi? He doesn't strike me as the Jedi type."

Chewbacca roared at her words and stormed out of the hut.

"Your challenge is that you must help Chewie with his chores . . ." Luke paused before adding, "without using the Force."

Rey's jaw dropped. She had not flown across the **galaxy** to do chores. But she realized the Luke was giving her a test and she was determined to pass it. "I accept your challenge. This should be easy. After all, I survived on Jakku without the Force for my whole life. One more day should be a breeze."

"We shall see," Luke said as Rey marched down the grassy hill on the island, chasing after Chewbacca.

Chewbacca ignored Rey as she followed him. Instead he picked up a pile of dirty laundry. Rey picked a pile up, too, but the clothes smelled like a stinky swamp. Holding her breath, Rey wondered if these were Luke's clothes from his time with Yoda on Dagobah.

Suddenly, a **porg** popped its head out from the laundry and gurgled a scream at Rey. Then an entire family of porgs jumped out of the clothes and scattered into other piles of dirty laundry that lay near Luke's hut.

"Hmm," Rey said. "Luke may be a great Jedi, but he doesn't know how to keep his place very clean."

Finally, Chewbacca stopped by a small crater filled with bubbling water. He tossed the clothes into the crater, then dripped one droplet of soap over the clothes. A whirlpool began to swirl in the crater to wash the laundry.

"Seems easy enough," said Rey as she found another crater and dropped the clothes inside.

A rumbling started shaking the ground as Chewbacca and a flock of porgs looked over at Rey and shook their heads.

"What did I do?" she asked. "Oh, right! I forgot to add soap."

Rey poured a big box of soap into the water. "There we go," she said.

An epic geyser burst out of the crater, launching Luke's clothes into the air. The porgs angrily ran around, collecting Luke's clothes.

"Okay, so maybe laundry isn't my thing," admitted Rey. "I've got this lightsaber. I could dice up some food for lunch if you'd like."

Chewbacca nodded and shuffled back toward the rock huts where Rey and Luke stayed. He leaned down to pick up some rocks to use to patch a new fence that had been knocked down by strong winds.

"Oh, I can help with this, I'm sure!" cheered Rey. She closed her eyes and focused on the rocks. The ground rumbled and suddenly several rocks levitated by themselves and re-formed, brick by brick, like a puzzle putting itself together until the fence had been mended.

Rey opened her eyes, ready to receive Chewbacca's thanks. But instead, Chewie was stuck on the other side of Rey's new and very tall wall. He stood on his tiptoes and peered at the young woman.

"Oh . . . Sorry," said Rey. "I was just trying to help . . . but it looks like I've blocked you out. I can fix it."

But Chewbacca shook his head and roared. Rey had done quite enough.

Chewie walked along the winding fence until he reached an opening. Then he tended to a garden that looked sad and full of weeds. Rey watched as the Wookiee pulled the weeds in order to help the vegetables and flowers grow. It seemed simple enough, but when Rey tried to pull the weeds, they refused to be picked. She found herself in a tug-of-war against the stubborn plants. Chewbacca shook his head at her again, but this only frustrated Rey.

"I promise, I can do something as easy as this," she said. Then, Rey flicked open her hand powerfully and felt the Force surge through her. With a mighty pull, the stuck weeds exploded out of the ground. Unfortunately, Rey had not pulled weeds; she had removed the roots to one of the only trees on the island. The tree tipped over and crashed down on top of the new fence that Rey had just made.

Chewbacca covered his eyes. Even Rey covered her eyes. Luke's challenge was proving to be more difficult than it seemed.

Rey bowed to Chewie and left for a short break. She was messing up this sacred island left and right. Perhaps Luke was right to refuse to teach her the ways of the Force when she first came here. Perhaps she was not ready to be a Jedi.

Then a strange sound floated through the countryside like a snarling beast. Chewbacca and a group of porgs ran and hid behind Rey.

The porgs pointed to a dark cave that Rey had never noticed before. The snarl rang out again, only it was louder and angrier this time.

"You have taken care of me during my stay," Rey told the Wookiee and his friends. "Now it is my turn to take care of you."

Rey ignited her lightsaber and walked toward the cave. Whatever was inside must have been pure evil — it sounded very scary.

As she stepped into the darkness of the secret cave, the strange noise stopped and was replaced with a smacking sound . . . followed by a yawn.

The shadow of an old man stretched across the cave walls. The snarls had belonged to her master, Luke Skywalker! He had finally found a moment of peace and quiet to take a well-deserved nap.

"Luke!" shouted Rey. "Are you sleeping? Or is this part of your training, like how Yoda trained you?"

Luke snapped awake. "Like Yoda?" Luke was confused. Then he smiled. "Yes, yes, yes! Exactly like how Yoda trained me. Why don't you go back to helping out around the island? I'm going to shut my eyes for a little longer while you, um, learn the ways of the Force by mowing the lawn, doing the dishes . . . just like Yoda taught me!"

The old Jedi closed his eyes and drifted back to sleep.

STORY #2:

DENGAR-3PO

Many years before Rey trained with Luke, in the crowded streets of Coruscant, a golden **droid** named C-3PO walked down the street. Coruscant was the biggest city in the galaxy, and the droid was looking into store windows. He peered through the windows and spoke into a **headset**. "I don't see **Dengar** anywhere, sir."

"Keep looking, Threepio," a voice in the headset said. "He's got to be there somewhere. Our sources say that he's on the planet and he's up to no good."

C-3PO passed another store. It was full of used engine parts for sale. "Master Anakin, may I ask you a question?"

Anakin Skywalker and Obi-Wan Kenobi stood atop a nearby building. Obi-Wan Kenobi was a powerful Jedi Knight, and Anakin was his **apprentice**. They watched the shiny droid through a set of **binoculars**. It was easy to spot him because he glared in the sun. They were looking for the dangerous bounty hunter named Dengar. It was important to keep a close eye on their friend.

"Sure, Threepio," Anakin answered. "What's on your mind?"

"What am I doing here?" C-3PO asked.

Obi-Wan spoke over the headset. "You are helping us, Threepio."

"Yes, but what I mean to ask is . . . why am I the one hunting for . . ." The droid stopped and looked around to make sure no one else was listening to him. Then he whispered, "Why am I the one hunting for Dengar?"

Dengar was a name that struck fear into the hearts of the bravest heroes and the most crooked criminals all over the galaxy. He was a mean bounty hunter who wasn't afraid of anything, including the Jedi. Anakin and Obi-Wan had received a report that he was visiting Coruscant, and whenever Dengar was in town, trouble wasn't far behind him.

"Dengar knows what we look like," explained Anakin. "But he doesn't know you. So, you are going to be our eyes on the ground, and as soon as you find him, Obi-Wan and I will surprise him and catch him."

C-3PO nodded, then paused outside of a clothing store. "But, sir, my chance of finding Dengar in one of these stores on this planet is —

"Don't worry about the odds," said Anakin. "Now, please be our eyes on the ground, not our mouths. You have to be quiet, or else you'll draw attention to yourself. Understand?"

"Loud and clear, Master Anakin."

The droid resumed his mission and checked the next store. It was a clothing shop, but it seemed empty. There was no one working in the store, so C-3PO went in to investigate.

"Hello? Is anyone here?" he asked, but there was no answer.

As he turned to leave, the droid noticed an odd-looking hat hanging up next to the door. It was a white hat, just like the one Dengar wore.

"Hmm," C-3PO wondered aloud. "I have always wondered why droids don't wear clothes. Anakin and Obi-wan seem to like wearing clothes. And Master Yoda loves his robe. Perhaps I should try on an outfit?"

C-3PO walked through the store again to make sure it was empty. Then he decided to try some clothes on. He found a purple, feathery boa and wrapped it around his neck.

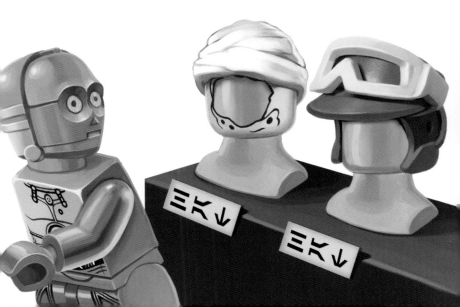

"Tee-hee," he laughed. "That tickles my circuits too much."

Next he tried on a robe. "Hmm, this would be better for bedtime." He put the robe and the boa back where he'd found them.

C-3PO then tried on a pair of brown pants. They were a little tight, but still flexible. Now he needed a pair of shoes. He found a nice pair of boots with rockets on the bottom of them.

"Well, those rockets might come in handy, won't they? Brilliant. What will they think of next?"

Then the droid tried on a shirt and found a gray backpack. He threw the backpack over his shoulders and moved stiffly toward the door, where he grabbed the white hat and set it on top of his chrome dome.

Admiring himself in the mirror, C-3PO couldn't wait to show Anakin and Obi-Wan his new outfit.

"Master Anakin, I think I've found something here," C-3PO said.

"Great, Threepio. Is it Dengar?" Anakin asked.

"See for yourself," said the clothed droid as he jumped from the store and presented himself in the direction of the Jedi. "Ta-da!"

But when Anakin and Obi-Wan looked through their binoculars, they did not see a well-dressed droid. They saw a mysterious stranger who looked an awful lot like Dengar.

"It's him!" Anakin hollered as he leapt into action.

Obi-Wan scrambled quickly after him. "Get out of there, Threepio!" Anakin yelled.

"Where?! Where?!" C-3PO flailed his arms in a panic and dropped his headset. "Where is Dengar? I don't see him anywhere! Oh, he is truly a master of disguise!"

Suddenly a laser blast exploded beside C-3PO on the right. Someone was firing a blaster cannon at him!

"Anakin!" said Obi-Wan. "You know I dislike blasters. Put it away and let's capture Dengar like true Jedi."

Anakin holstered his blaster and ran alongside his teacher. "Sounds good!"

As they chased C-3PO, thinking he was Dengar, the Jedi caught up to him quickly.

"I don't remember a bounty hunter ever being this slow," said Obi-Wan. "Do you?"

Anakin shook his head. "No way . . . which means he's probably setting a trap for us. Keep your eyes peeled."

C-3PO rounded another corner but was met with a dead end. A gate separated him from freedom and trapped him with his attackers.

"Not so fast!" Anakin yelled as he drew his lightsaber. Obi-Wan did the same.

Quickly, C-3PO turned on his rocket boots and blasted upward. The droid waved his arms to catch his balance, but the rockets were too strong.

"He's getting away," said Obi-Wan.

"I don't think so . . . Just watch." Anakin and Obi-Wan turned off their lightsabers and watched the costumed stranger, who had lost his balance and was now rocketing toward the ground. He landed with a thud.

Anakin and Obi-Wan walked over to their new prisoner.

"Well, well, well, if it isn't the diabolical Dengar," said Anakin as he pulled off the white hat.

"Actually, it isn't," said C-3PO.

"Threepio!" exclaimed Anakin. "What are you doing here? Why are you wearing Dengar's outfit? Where did you find this stuff?"

The droid pointed back to the clothing store. "Over there, sir."

As Anakin turned around, he saw the clothing store. It was right next to a Coruscant bank.

Suddenly, there was an explosion and Dengar walked out of the smoke carrying bags of money. With a wave to the Jedi, he escaped in the other direction.

"Oh boy," said Anakin. "Let's not mention this to Yoda."

STORY #3:

NOW, THIS IS PODRACING!

Years after the adventure with Dengar, Luke Skywalker, the son of Anakin Skywalker (now Darth Vader), was heading back home to **Tatooine**. As part of his Jedi training, Luke was expected to have strong control over his emotions and always remember the little things. He should have been on the lookout for danger, but he kept thinking about his days growing up on this desert planet.

As he piloted his X-wing down toward Tatooine, his faithful droid unit, **R2-D2**, beeped a low warning.

"I know, Artoo," said Luke. "It's not safe here, but there's something I have to do."

The small droid buzzed again.

"No, it's not a rebel mission." Luke checked his location on the controls. "It's kind of personal. Just keep a lookout, okay? You never know when the Empire is going to rear its ugly head."

Artoo cooed as Luke set on the afterburners and steered his ship into Tatooine's atmosphere. The sand that covered the ground hadn't changed one bit. Luke hadn't been back since he first met Han Solo and Chewie.

Luke scanned the horizon. There were no stormtroopers to be seen. Either they were very good at hiding, or Luke had gotten lucky. And something told him that he hadn't gotten lucky.

In the distance, a city appeared. It looked like a mirage, shimmering under the intense heat of the planet's two bright suns. But Luke knew that it wasn't a mirage. This was the city of Mos Eisley: the last place he'd been on this planet before leaving for the wildest adventure of his life.

A whistle came from Luke's copilot. "Yes, Artoo, I remember how dangerous this city is. But I'm almost a Jedi now. I can handle myself. We'll be in and out in no time, before you can say, '*Darth Vader dons dark robes every day*' three times fast."

R2-D2 bleeped in frustration.

"We're going in, Artoo," Luke said. "Get ready to land in the sand."

The spaceship touched down on a sandy airstrip, and Luke jumped out first. As R2-D2 scooted next to him, Luke gave him a look.

"Hmm, you're going to need a disguise for this mission," said Luke. He pulled out a beret from behind his back and set it on top of the droid. Then he grabbed a pen and drew a fancy, twirling mustache on the front of R2-D2. Last, Luke found a drop cloth in the hangar, folded it into a poncho, and draped it over the droid.

Luke stepped back to admire his work. "There, that's better. Of course, it's a good thing there's low lighting in the place we're going. Oh, and when we get there, better let me do all the talking."

The Mos Eisley cantina was not a safe place for droids. Luke remembered this from his last visit. It was, however, a great place to find trouble. As Luke and R2-D2 entered the cantina, the same music was playing as the last time they were there. Luke walked up to the bar and waved the bartender over.

"I need to see your lost-and-found box," he said hypnotically.

"You need to see our lost-and-found box," the man said. And under the charm of the Force, he pulled a giant box out from behind the bar.

Luke began to search through the lost-and-found. He found lots of interesting items at the top, but none of them were what he was looking for. He dug deeper and deeper until he finally felt something furry.

Victoriously, Luke lifted a long, hairy ball of fuzz over his head. "I found it!"

"And I found you." A red lightsaber sparked to life. In its dangerous glow, the black mask of Darth Vader appeared out of the shadows.

"Wait, what is that disgusting thing?"

"It's not disgusting," said Luke. "It's my lucky **bantha** braid!"

"Ew, gross. I am wearing a mask and I can still smell it from here," said Darth Vader. "Well, it's not your lucky day today, young rebel scum. You're surrounded."

Stormtroopers were guarding every exit. Still, Luke couldn't help but smile. He thought the Empire might come for him, which was exactly why he'd brought R2-D2.

Without warning, Luke swiftly pulled the beret and poncho off of R2-D2. Everyone in the Mos Eisley cantina gasped.

"You know the rules!" the man behind the bar yelled. "No droids allowed!"

Instantly, the cantina erupted into a brawl, as the cantina's employees all lifted the blue-and-white droid off the ground.

"Sorry, Artoo," said Luke as he mixed in with the angry crowd.

"Where did Skywalker go?!" screamed Darth Vader. "Stop them, you fools!"

The cantina workers were too strong. They pushed past the stormtroopers and threw the droid out into the street, blocking the entry as they did. Luke popped out from the crowd and helped R2-D2 back up.

"We've got to get out of here, fast!" Luke screamed as they raced away.

The streets were filled with stormtroopers searching for rebels. Luke and R2-D2 sneaked down the alleyways until they realized that they couldn't get back to their hanger without being spotted.

Then Luke noticed a poster that read: PODRACER PILOTS WANTED FOR A RACE TODAY.

He smiled at R2-D2 and clipped his lucky bantha braid to his shirt. "Okay, it's time for plan P . . . as in podracing!"

They sneaked over to the starting line and climbed into a podracer's cockpit. R2-D2 let out a high-pitched whistle.

"I know," said Luke as he looked at the two thrusters that sat in front of the cockpit. "I'd say that this was like riding a landspeeder but that would be a lie. Hopefully we'll only have to make one loop on the track, and we should be able to reach our ship to escape."

"That's a good plan." The evil voice came from the podracer next to them. It was Darth Vader. "Too bad I'm one of the all-time best podracers. First, I'll beat you in the race, then I'll make sure that all of your rebel friends know that you are a loser."

"You'll have to catch us first!" said Luke as he engaged the podracer thrusters and exploded into the lead.

"Hey, that's not fair!" screamed Vader. He revved his engines and chased after Luke.

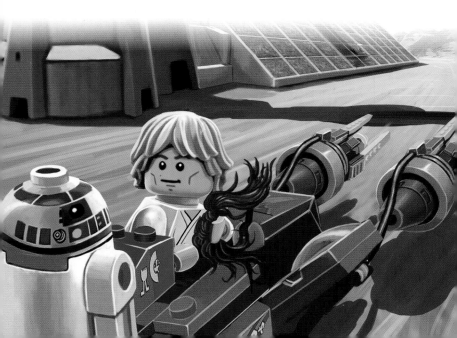

The podracers weaved through the more dangerous parts of Tatooine. Luke was fast, but Darth Vader was faster. True to his words, the Sith Lord was a very good podracer. As Vader inched closer to Luke and R2-D2, he rammed into them, sending them off course. Luke tried to pull his podracer back, but he slammed into the side of a building and ricocheted back.

"We can't take another blow like that," Luke cried to Artoo. "Come on, lucky bantha braid, we need your help!"

Just as Darth Vader was making a move to ram Luke again, a bunch of other podracers came speeding from behind them!

"You crazy cheaters started without us!" the other pilots yelled. "And we hate cheaters!"

Suddenly two podracers pulled ahead of Darth Vader and slammed on their brakes. Vader was forced to slow down, which gave Luke and Artoo an opening. They blasted into high gear.

"Enough of this!" said Vader as he waved his fist in the air, and a Force push broke both podracers into a hundred pieces.

With a clear path, Vader set out after Luke again. "You won't get away this time!"

Luke was traveling so fast now, he wished he had worn a pair of goggles. His wind-whipped hair was getting in his face and making it very hard to see. He turned to spot Vader catching up to them.

"HELP US, BANTHA BRAID!" Luke screamed as a strong gust of wind blasted by, grabbing his lucky bantha braid and sending it flying through the air.

"Oh no." Vader gulped as the stringy, disgusting chunk of hair floated for a moment, then snaked directly into his engines, which instantly died on impact. Darth Vader's podracer fell straight into the dirt.

"YEAH!" Luke cheered. "I knew my lucky bantha braid would come in handy! Now let's circle back and get it. I don't want to lose that braid twice."

R2-D2 beeped and took over the controls. If there was one thing that droid knew, it was that Luke's lucky charm was better off lost.

Welcome to First Order School

Hi, I'm **Kylo Ren**. I'm good at using the Force and even better at having cool hair! I want to tell you all about the training school we call "**First Order** School." That's where you train to join me in the First Order. Here are three stories from the recent year to think about before you apply!

STORY #4:

FIRST DAY AT THE FIRST ORDER

Today a brand-new class of students had begun their training at First Order School! These **stormtroopers** had one goal in mind: to become great soldiers for the First Order! They needed to prove they were smart enough and evil enough to fight for Kylo Ren.

When they started school, the troopers were given classroom supplies. Each student received notebooks, folders, and blasters. They also got space pencils to take notes with. Those pencils were very important because, unlike pens, they work when there is no gravity! A trooper never knows when they might find themselves floating upside down. It's always good to be prepared.

Once the students had their supplies, they gathered in homeroom. A tiny image of someone lit up at the front of the class. It was a 3-D image called a **hologram**, of **Supreme Leader Snoke**! Snoke was the leader of the First Order. He was holding a remote control that let him adjust the hologram.

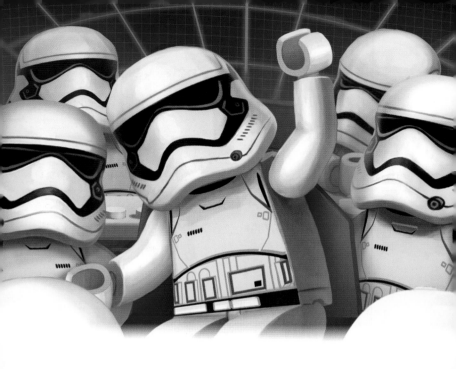

"Yes, yes, I know, it's an honor to see me," Snoke said. "Sit down. Welcome to First Order School. Your training here will be fun and dangerous. And as you begin your classes, you might have questions . . ."

One of the troopers raised her hand and asked, "Sir, Supreme Leader Snoke, sir, I have a question. You are much smaller than I thought you would be."

"That is not a question!" Snoke yelled. Snoke looked at the remote control he was holding. "Now, what's going on here . . . oh darn. I set this thing to tiny mode."

With the press of a button, Snoke's hologram grew until his head nearly touched the ceiling. "Now, where was I? Ah yes. As you enter your lessons, you might have questions . . . DO NOT ASK ANY QUESTIONS! Follow my orders. And as of today, I order you to . . . enjoy yourselves."

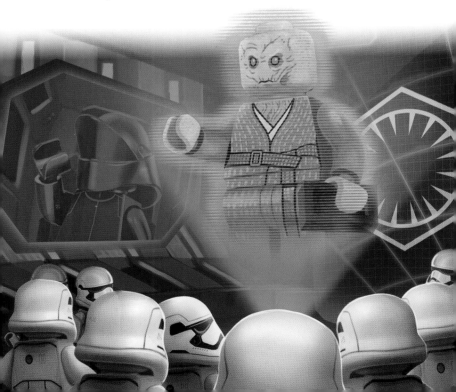

The troopers jumped up and cheered again. Then, with a smile, Snoke said, "Just kidding. I order you to work hard, study your helmets off, and become part of the First Order, which will wipe out the **Resistance** once and for all! But before that, you have gym class. Please join your teacher, Kylo Ren, in the **gymnasium** to begin your training."

Snoke clicked another button, and the giant hologram disappeared. Standing behind him was a very tall First Order trooper dressed in silver armor with a cape draped over her shoulder. It was **Captain Phasma**. She was one of the toughest captains of the First Order.

"Let's go, kiddos," said Phasma. "Kylo Ren doesn't like to be kept waiting. As you may have heard, patience is not what he is known for."

As the troops entered the gym, they saw that it was huge, filled with giant red First Order banners and blinking computers. In the middle of the floor, Kylo was waiting, surrounded by a bunch of metal balls! The metal balls were actually tiny droids.

Kylo held up one hand to get everyone's attention. A tiny droid flew up and landed in his hand. "Today, you are going to play a game called Droid Dodgeball," Kylo said. "It's just like regular dodgeball, except the balls fly around and try to zap you with a laser. If you get zapped, you're out. Last one standing wins. The game starts now!"

HELLO, CLASS . . .

All the droids flew into the air, firing lasers. Some troopers were hit right away, and an alarm sounded to tell them that they were out of the game. The troopers ran around, bumping into one another and getting hit by the lasers over and over again. Kylo thought it was very funny.

Kylo stood in the center of the room, laughing. Then, one trooper tried to use a notebook to block a laser. The laser bounced off his notepad and hit Kylo, burning his hair.

"YEE-OUCH!" he screamed. All the droids stopped immediately. They knew they'd made a big mistake. Kylo didn't like anyone messing up his cool, long hair.

Kylo turned on his red **lightsaber** and leapt after the droids. The troopers cheered as he flipped and flew through the gym and destroyed all the droids. As the last droid flew away, Kylo threw his lightsaber like a spear. The droid broke as Kylo's lightsaber smashed into the wall. But . . . his lightsaber also destroyed the gravity control in the gym. Everyone floated into the air, stuck in zero gravity.

As Kylo floated above the ground, he saw what he'd actually done to the gym. The gym was covered with wrecked droids and metal pieces.

"Students," he said while upside down. "Use your space pens to take this important note: You must never tell Supreme Leader Snoke what happened here today. This is the third gym I've destroyed this week, so let's make this our little secret. Okay?"

"Yes, sir!" the troops all cheered as they wrote in their books.

Kylo nodded. "Great. And now, for your next challenge, uh . . . rebuild the gym and clean up this mess. Actually, you should probably get used to cleaning up our messes. So, you *are* learning something important!"

STORY #5:

CAPTAIN PHASMA'S WILD RIDE

Every First Order trooper dreams of being a pilot. There's nothing like flying through space in a **TIE fighter** battle against a team of rebels. But before new troops face off against expert pilots, like **Poe Dameron**, they need to start small.

It was a day like any other in the halls of First Order School, and a new trooper had just been told he wasn't ready to fly yet. "No way!" he said. He flapped his arms and pretended

to zoom past his friends. "I'm ready to fly right now! Look out, galaxy, here I come!"

Another trooper joined in, running around the other troops: "I'm right behind you, partner!"

The two new recruits jumped down the hallway until they tripped over each other and fell. They rolled until Captain Phasma stopped them.

The fearless leader shook her head slowly. "So you think you can fly?" she asked. "Piloting a TIE fighter isn't as simple as bouncing around a hallway with your friends. If you think you're ready, then let's begin the TIE fighter driver's training course."

The troopers scrambled back to their feet and saluted Captain Phasma. "We're ready to take the wheel!"

"We will see," snapped the captain as she turned and walked toward the space deck.

The students followed her, cheering. The space deck was giant. TIE fighters and other battleships were parked on the floor and along the walls on each side. Trained First Order troopers saluted the captain as she entered the runway. At the end of the runway, an opening showed the galaxy full of stars.

WHEEEE!

"Wow," said one of the students. "I cannot believe we're about to fly an actual TIE fighter!"

"No one is actually flying a TIE fighter yet," Captain Phasma said. "You troopers didn't think that I was going to let you fly alone the very first time you set foot in a TIE fighter, did you?"

"Kind of," another student said.

"Well, then you are *kind* of wrong," said the captain. "Besides, it's trash day. There are garbage ships carrying trash outside, and you don't want to run into them. No, you will take a pretend flight, a **simulation**. We'll start with something easy, like an **asteroid belt**. Asteroids are space rocks that can hurt your ship, and you need to learn how to dodge them. It will feel like you are flying, but you will be safely tied to the space deck. The last thing we want is for any of these ships to get hurt."

One by one, the students climbed into TIE fighters that were tied to a wall. The inside of the spaceship was small. There was room for only two pilots. One pilot flew the ship, while the other was in charge of the cannons.

With the troopers aboard, Captain Phasma went to a space traffic control booth overlooking the deck to talk to the pilots. "Remember to buckle up, everyone. Safety first, even in a battle simulation."

The recruits clicked themselves into place. "Ready for action!"

"We are starting the TIE fighters now," said Captain Phasma.

Each of the TIE fighters began to hum as the engines warmed up. The troopers all cheered. "Whee! Even if we're not flying today, this is so cool!"

In the air traffic control booth, Captain Phasma ordered a trooper to prepare the asteroid battle simulation.

A trooper nodded to the captain. "Simulation ready on your command, ma'am."

"Now," said Captain Phasma, and the trooper pressed a button.

Suddenly, all of the TIE fighters blasted into space!

Phasma ran to the control booth window and watched as the training pilots flew out of sight. "Who would like to tell me why my simulation just actually launched First Order students into space without any flying experience?" she asked.

The control deck went quiet until the trooper who pressed the button spoke: "Oh, here's the problem. I hit the launch button instead of the launch *simulation* button. Hmm, maybe it's not a good idea to have those two buttons right next to each other . . . and they're the same color, too. Very confusing."

Captain Phasma yelled, "Remind me to make it less confusing for you when I get back!"

She ran out of the room and jumped inside another TIE fighter. She fired it up and flew after her new recruits, who were already far ahead of her.

"WHOA! This feels so real!" said one trooper in a pilot seat.

Another trooper reported in over the headset: "Hey, guys, it looks like we've reached the asteroid belt!"

A cluster of asteroids hovered outside of his front windshield as the trooper took the steering controls. He swerved down, barely missing the first rock chunk. He weaved the ship in and out of giant **boulders**. "Wow, if this was real, I'd be so scared right now!" he said.

Another voice interrupted their radios: "All recruits stay where you are and do not, under any circumstances, shift into **hyperdrive**, unless you want to never fly again!"

"Uh-oh, that's Captain Phasma," said one trooper. "And she does not sound happy."

Suddenly, a net swooped over the ships and pulled them safely from the asteroid belt. The same net caught each and every TIE fighter that had a First Order student inside. As the pilots looked up, they saw the net attached to another TIE fighter, which expertly flew through space. Captain Phasma sat in the pilot's seat.

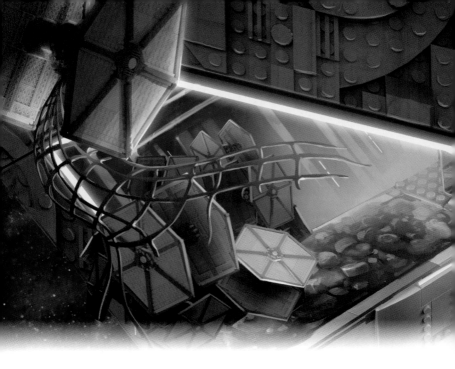

"Now I need to get you all back before Kylo knows we're missing," Captain Phasma told the others.

But when they were almost back to the space deck, another giant ship took off—a huge trash ship! The captain of the giant ship turned quickly to avoid them, but she couldn't get out of the way in time. All the TIE fighters plunged deep into a pile of trash aboard the garbage ship.

Back on the space deck, Kylo Ren had just arrived to see what all the commotion was about. He waved to Captain Phasma as she exited her filthy TIE fighter.

"I never thought your flying stunk, Phasma," said Kylo as he coughed at the smell. "But you are out to prove me wrong."

Captain Phasma held her head high. "I might not have the best of luck when it comes to landing in garbage," she said, "but I always live to fight another day!"

STORY #6:

The Best *Worst* Villain

While training to fight Wookiees and rebels might sound dangerous, it's nothing compared to lunchtime at First Order School. The troopers are treated to three meals a day, prepared by the worst cooks in the galaxy.

One day at lunch, two students stared at their awful food. On their trays, a dusty piece of bread floated in a sea of green glop.

"What is this supposed to be?" asked one of the troopers.

"According to the menu, it's macaroni and cheese," said the other trooper. She couldn't believe the bad smell coming from such a small amount of food. "Ugh, what are they trying to do to us by feeding us this disgusting gunk?"

"Good question," said the first trooper. "It's like they give us this horrible stuff on purpose. Maybe this nasty food is supposed to make us meaner, angrier, and every bit as bitter as what's on our trays?"

EEEWW . . .

The second trooper nodded in agreement. "It's like they say: 'You are what you eat.' And if we eat the most evil food, then we'll become the most evil troopers ever. It could even be part of our training!"

The first trooper lifted the spoon up to his mouth before stopping and letting the food drop back down. "Gah, I can't eat it," he said. "Since when is macaroni and cheese green? And sure, our armor is stain resistant, but if I spill any of this food on me, I'll never get the smell out."

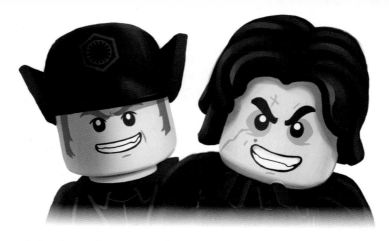

"Yeah, I know," the second trooper said. "You know who probably loves this stuff? Kylo Ren. He's so evil he probably thinks this slop tastes as sweet as candy."

The other trooper shook his head. "That's where you're wrong. **General Hux** probably eats way more gross food than Kylo Ren. He is way more evil than Kylo. He commands the First Order army, and he blew up an entire star system!"

"That is pretty evil," said the trooper as she pushed the food around her tray. "But Kylo Ren destroyed the Jedi. That was also pretty evil."

"I suppose we'll never know who is more evil, Kylo Ren or General Hux," the first trooper admitted. "Unless we see them eat this food!"

The two troopers jumped up and ran across the **cafeteria** searching for Kylo and Hux. They found both of the leaders sitting at a table together. Kylo had his mask off as he talked to Hux. Neither of them expected the troopers to interrupt their lunch, which was way better than what the troopers ate.

"Excuse me, your villainous sirs," the first trooper said. "My friend and I have a question for you both. We were wondering which of you is the evilest of all?"

The leaders looked at each other and laughed.

"That has to be the worst question I've ever heard," said General Hux. "Wouldn't you agree, Kylo?"

"Definitely the worst question," said Kylo. "I'm the evilest villain of all. Everyone knows that."

Suddenly, General Hux's laughter stopped. "Oh, Kylo, don't be so silly. I'm the evilest **villain** of all. Sure, you are mysterious, moody, and you have the whole Force thing working for you, but at the end of the day, I'm the biggest bad guy around here."

A crowd of troopers gathered around the leaders' lunch table. This was the most interesting thing to ever happen in the First Order cafeteria.

"It sounds like we need to have a contest to prove, once and for all, who is the evilest," suggested Kylo.

"You're on!" said Hux. "What should we do to prove who's better at being the worst?"

The first trooper waved his arm in the air. "I know! I know! You can eat the cafeteria lunch today! Whoever finishes first has to be the most vile villain ever."

At this suggestion, Kylo and Hux both gagged and turned as green as the macaroni and cheese.

"I've got a better idea," Kylo announced. "We'll have three challenges, and the winner is the worst. First, I challenge you to a scare game, Hux. Whoever scares the most troopers wins."

General Hux cracked a crooked smile. "I'll go first. Any trooper in this room who isn't scared right now will be forced to clean out the cafeteria kitchen . . . and take out the trash for a week!"

A **quivering** gasp filled the room as every trooper's stomach collectively let out a gross gurgle.

"That settles that," said Hux. "I'm clearly the winner here."

"Not so fast." Kylo reached under the table, and in one swift move, he put on his mask and turned on his lightsaber. The **jagged** edge of its red blade heated up the room and scared several troopers out of their actual **uniforms**— helmets, pants, and all!

Even General Hux flinched with fear.

"Point, Kylo Ren," the **cloaked** leader said in a distorted voice from underneath his mask. "The second challenge is up to you, Hux."

The general smoothed back his red hair. "Let's have a good, old-fashioned race, then. The first evildoer to cross the finish line wins. Troopers, form a finish line at the end of the lunchroom. We will break through you to win."

"What does a race have to do with being evil?" asked Kylo Ren.

"Line up at the starting point here and find out." General Hux bent into a racing position. "Unless you're too scared to race me?"

Kylo put his lightsaber away and leapt over the table, landing right next to Hux. "I'm not afraid of a footrace."

The troopers counted off all together: "On your mark, get set, GO!"

Kylo Ren bolted into an early lead by using the Force to freeze General Hux for a moment. But the general was fast—just as Kylo almost reached the finish line, Hux grabbed Ren's hood and tossed him backward. Kylo Ren landed on his bottom with a thud as Hux ran to victory, crashing through the troopers and knocking all of them down like bowling pins.

The troopers knew that using the Force to win was evil, but Hux using Ren's own fancy outfit to win the race and humiliate him added insult to injury.

"Looks like we're tied," said General Hux. "There's only one challenge left: a **duel**."

"A lightsaber duel?" Kylo laughed. "You have got to be kidding. I'd take you down faster than you took me down in that race."

"No, a blaster duel," explained General Hux. "We'll set up targets and whoever blasts the most will win."

"Or you could just eat the food," suggested the first trooper.

"A blaster duel it is!" both Hux and Kylo said at the same time.

General Hux went first, ordering several troopers to hold their cafeteria trays above their heads as targets. Hux quickly blasted the center of each tray. The troopers all cheered, even the ones who now had green macaroni and cheese spilled all over them.

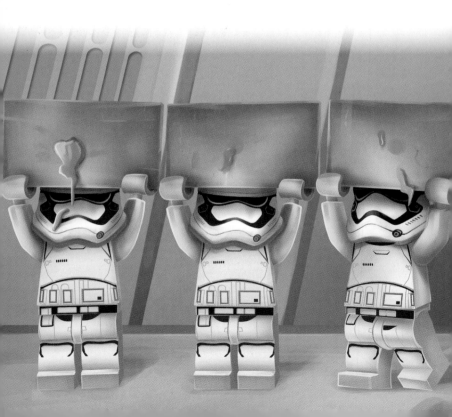

"Your turn, Kylo," said General Hux as he motioned for the green-slimed troopers to raise several more tray targets.

"I thought this was supposed to be a challenge," said Kylo as he pulled off his mask. "Hitting targets with your eyes open is one thing, but doing it with your eyes closed is something else."

Placing his helmet down, Kylo Ren shut his eyes and fired, with the Force guiding his aim. He struck the first four targets but missed the fifth! His final blast bounced off the lunchroom walls until it hurled back into the kitchen and exploded.

The room went silent. Then, Hux laughed. "What a rotten shot that was, Kylo! You missed the last target completely!"

Kylo Ren winked. "Did I?" he asked. "Let's ask the troopers. Did I miss my target, or did I just **annihilate** the awful food you have to eat every day?"

The First Order students swarmed in and lifted Kylo on their shoulders. "Three cheers for Kylo Ren, the destroyer of bad cafeteria food!"

"Sorry, Hux," said Ren as he turned on his lightsaber again. "It looks like the troops pick me. Okay, everyone, we're ordering out for lunch! Who likes pizza? I can slice it up for you!"

THE END

GLOSSARY

AHCH-TO: A planet pronounced "Ock-Toe," not "Achoo!"

ANAKIN SKYWALKER: A famous Jedi Knight who turned to the dark side and became Darth Vader.

ANNIHILATE: To completely defeat.

APPRENTICE: Someone who works with a mentor to get experience.

ASTEROID BELT: A group of rocks found in outer space.

BANTHA: A large, furry, elephant-like animal.

BINOCULARS: A device that lets people see things that are very far away.

BOULDER: A big, round rock.

CAFETERIA: A place to eat where food is served at a counter and then taken to tables.

CAPTAIN PHASMA: A female stormtrooper commander who works under Kylo Ren and General Hux.

CLOAK: A long, loose piece of outer clothing.

DENGAR: An evil bounty hunter.

DROID: A type of mechanical robot used for chores and other tasks.

DUEL: A fight between two people.

FIRST ORDER: An evil group led by Supreme Leader Snoke that wants to take over the galaxy.

FORCE: An invisible energy that binds the universe together and can be used by those who are Force-sensitive to move objects or sense attacks before they happen.

GALAXY: All the stars and planets where the events in *Star Wars* take place.

GENERAL HUX: The leader of the First Order army.

GYMNASIUM: A large, indoor room used for sports.

HEADSET: A device used to hold an earphone and microphone to someone's face, letting them talk to and listen to others.

HOLOGRAM: A 3-D picture made using light.

HYPERDRIVE: A system that lets spaceships fly faster than the speed of light, so they can move between very long distances in a short period of time.

JAGGED: Having sharp or uneven surfaces.

KYLO REN: A Force user and former Jedi trainee who left the Jedi to join the First Order.

LIGHTSABER: A laser sword used by people who also use the Force.

LUKE SKYWALKER: A Tatooine farm boy who became a great Jedi Knight.

POE DAMERON: A commander in the Resistance who is a very good pilot.

PORG: A species of cute, chubby birds.

QUIVER: To shake all over.

RESISTANCE: A small force led by General Leia Organa created to fight the First Order.

R2-D2:

A resourceful repair droid.

REY: A Force-sensitive human.

SIMULATION: A pretend exercise of something that looks like it's real.

STORMTROOPER: Soldiers of the First Order.

SUPREME LEADER SNOKE: The leader of the First Order and powerful user of the dark side of the Force.

TATOOINE: A harsh desert world orbiting twin suns in the galaxy's Outer Rim.

TIE FIGHTER: The star fighter spaceship used by the First Order.

UNIFORM: A set of clothing given out to a group that is the same for everyone in the group.

VILLAIN: A character who fights against heroes.

WOOKIEE: A tall, hairy creature. Chewbacca is a famous Wookiee.

LEGO® BRICK ADVENTURES

ENJOY THESE OTHER
LEGO BRICK ADVENTURES TITLES!